by Dale Wagner

RoseDog🐾Books
PITTSBURGH, PENNSYLVANIA 15238

RoseDog Books
585 Alpha Drive
Suite 103
Pittsburgh, PA 15238
Visit our website at www.rosedogbookstore.com

ISBN: 978-1-6366-1024-5
eISBN: 978-1-6366-1083-2

This
Old
Dime

*B*ack in the early 1970's my friend Jack and I would walk to the 7-11 convenience store after school. Some days, when we had no money, we would walk through the woods and collect empty soda bottles. You could redeem these bottles and collect 3 cents per bottle.

One day we were walking down the hill heading to the store. I was always looking for something as we walked and talked. All of a sudden I spotted this old dime. It was laying in the gutter amongst the leaves. I was very excited. I picked up the dime and took a look at it. It was old and worn out. The date on the dime was 1921. Jack looked at the dime, and we both thought it was really cool. I put the dime in the small pocket of my blue jeans to keep it separate from my other change. I did not want to accidentally spend it.

That evening I was in my room listening to a James Taylor eight track on my brother's stereo. I started to think about the old dime I had found. I pulled the dime out of my pocket and began to look at it.

I wondered why the edges were so worn out. Then I figured it must have been handled thousands of times, if not millions. Where had this dime been? What could you buy for 10 cents in the 1920's? What about the 1930's, 1940's, and 1950's? I began to think that cumulatively this dime could have purchased thousands of dollars of bread, milk, coffee, soda and no telling what else.

This old dime was probably jumping in and out of cash registers all day – every day, for years and decades.

This old dime was brand new at the end of W.W.I. I wonder if a dough-boy had this old dime in his pocket.

This old dime was popular in the "Roaring 20's." I wonder if a flapper ever used it.

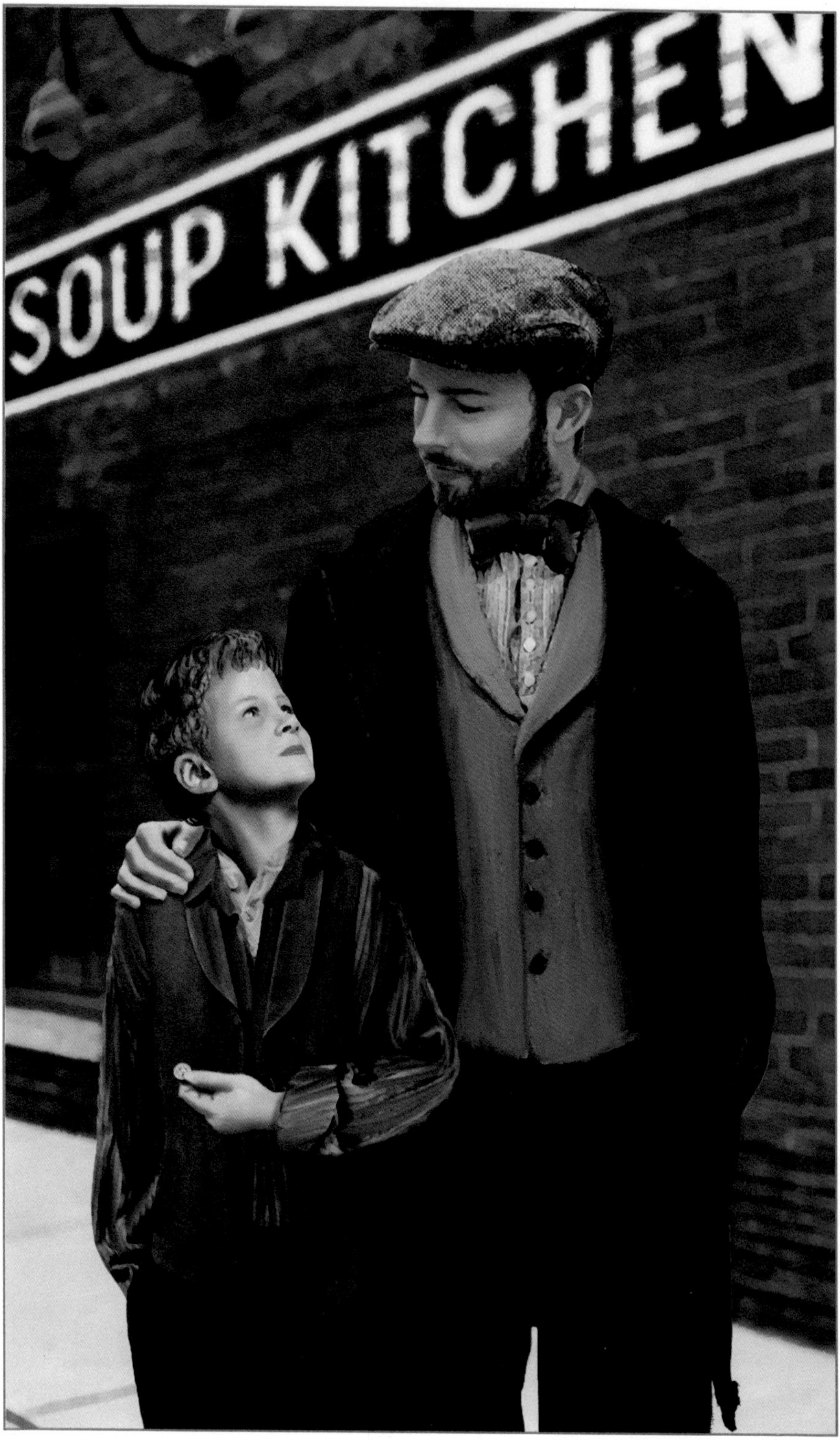
SOUP KITCHEN

Oh dear, don't forget about the great depression. The great depression started in 1929, when the stock market crashed. Millions of people lost all of their money, they lost their jobs and much more. People could not afford to buy food. All over the country people would line up to get a cup of soup. I bet some of those people would have loved to have this old dime.

Polio invaded our country and had become a devastating and crippling disease. In the 1930's President Franklin Roosevelt founded, "The March of Dimes". People collection millions of dimes to help pay for research to eradicate this disease.

I bet this old dime helped in that cause.

In 1946 President Roosevelt's image was placed on the dime to honor him for his work with The March of Dimes.

Our country was involved in WWII be-
tween 1941 and 1945. This old dime was
still very popular and valuable. It continued
to jump in and out of cash registers at a fe-
verish pace. It was also going into vending
machines, and pay telephones. You could
buy a cup of Joe for 10 cents.

All through the 1950's people all over the country were using this old dime on a constant basis. It has been in thousands of peoples' pockets, and change purses. I am starting to understand why the edges are so worn.

In the 1960's our country was involved in the Vietnam War. I wonder if this old dime went to Vietnam and later returned.

We landed on the moon in 1969.

I don't think this old dime went to the moon but it could have.

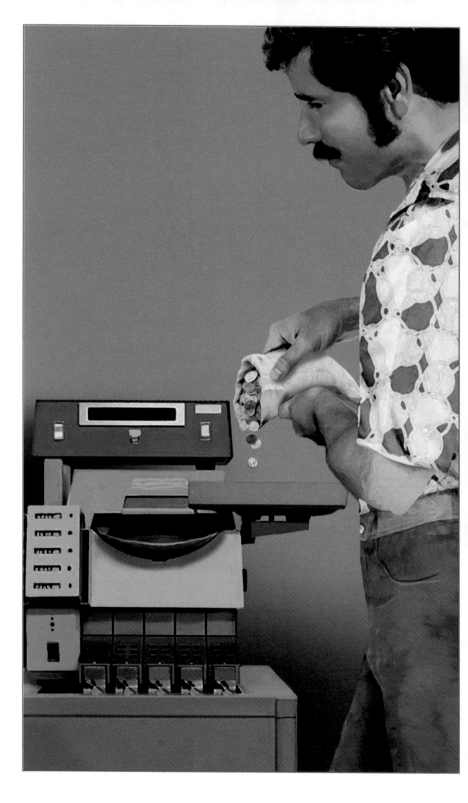

During the 1970's is when I found this old dime. It had started to lose its glamour and value by this time. People would cash in old dimes for their silver value. Millions of old dimes were melted down and recycled into other things. This old dime had survived.

I really started to like this old dime even though it was worn out. I decided to keep it. I put this old dime in a small box. I continued to collect old coins and put the coins in another box.

Now this old dime rest in a small box inside a bigger box, that is inside a suitcase that is in a trunk in my attic.

If this old dime could talk, the stories of where it has been, and what it has seen would be endless.